How
and D

CW00821766

The building of the upper dams
of the Derwent Valley Water Board

by

Professor Brian Robinson,

M.Sc., Ph.D., D.Sc.

Dedication

To the memory of my maternal grandfather,

"Long" George Green, a former navvy and a gentle man

The DVWB's engine "Nogi" was delivered new ex-works on 31 March 1905 to Bole Hill Quarry (vide infra) where it was to work before being transferred to Howden in 1910, whence it moved to Derwent in the latter half of 1913. It is seen here, circa 1912, in the upper Derwent Valley. The engine drivers and their crews took great pride in their locomotives, with even the coupling links being regularly polished and greased. For this photograph, they have greased the engine's side facing the camera and then have decorated it by hand with a scaling effect, led by its driver, the tallest of the three men on the footplate, "Long" George Green. When she was only a few years old, his eldest daughter, Violet Mary, the author's late mother, often accompanied her father on journeys over the Bamford & Howden Railway between the Howden site and "Waterworks' Sidings" (vide infra) in this locomotive.

Setting the Scene

A fresh and potable running supply of water to our homes is today so often taken for granted and is a most precious commodity that is so often misused and wasted by a greedy and thoughtless society.

Consequent upon the Industrial Revolution, there was a rapid proliferation in the urban populations of the expanding industrial towns and cities of Britain. These thereby demanded increases in their water supplies on a scale that could usually be best satisfied by damming mountain valleys and constructing aqueducts from the impounded reservoirs to permit flow under gravity to lesser reservoirs on elevated sites close to the places that were to be supplied. Thus it was that, during the nineteenth century, towns and cities on all sides of the Peak District began to look toward its moors (gritstone areas of high rainfall and high water-retaining propensity), rivers and valleys as a means of augmenting their supplies of water.

Sheffield, to the east, was the first to do so – during the 1830s – with its Redmires Middle Reservoir (on Hallam Moor), Rivelin Reservoirs and Lower and Upper Redmire Reservoirs being impounded during 1836, 1848, 1849 and 1854, respectively. Furthermore, in 1853 it obtained powers for the construction of dams in the Loxley Valley, as a result of which dams at Dale Dyke, Damflask, Agden and Strines were completed in 1875 (the first Dale Dyke Dam, which was about ¼ mile downstream of the present structure, rapidly collapsed around midnight on Friday, 11 March 1864, shortly after its completion – indeed, whilst the reservoir was still filling – and led to what still remains the worst ever British dam failure, with the flood wave of some 700 million gallons causing widespread devastation and havoc in Low Bradfield, Damflask, Loxley, Malin Bridge, Owlerton, Neepsend and Hillsborough, and killing 244 people, 102 of these being from the populous then village of Malin Bridge, some 5 miles downstream of the dam), 1867 (but a leakage discovered as the reservoir was filling caused its use to be postponed in order that necessary remedial works

could be carried out), 1869 and 1871, respectively. In 1897 the valley of the Little Don was dammed, with reservoirs at Langsett and Underbank (outside the present National Park) being commissioned in 1905 and 1907, respectively. On the opposite side of the Park, ingressions by Manchester and Salford began in 1846, with the damming of the River Etherow in the Longdendale Valley and the impounding of the Woodhead, Torside, Rhodeswood, Vale House and Bottoms Reservoirs between 1848-1865, 1849-1869, 1849-1852, 1865-1869 and 1869-1877, respectively, in their day the world's largest cascade of reservoirs to be impounded. Later, and again to the District's western side, Stockport's Kinder Reservoir was completed in 1912, followed by its dams in the Goyt Valley. To the Peak District's northeast, Huddersfield built the Bilberry Dam during the 1840s and its Wessenden Head, Wessenden Old, Blakely and Butterley Reservoirs were completed in 1881, 1890, 1903 and 1906, respectively, and other Yorkshire Woollen Districts were supplied from reservoirs at Dunford Bridge (1858), Lower Windleden (1872), Yateholme (1874), Riding Wood (1874), Upper Windleden (1890), Harden (1899) and Snailsden (1899). To the northwest of the Peak District, the Saddleworth area was supplied by the Yeoman Hey, Greenfield, Chew and Dove Stone Reservoirs which were brought into service in 1880, 1903, 1912 and 1967, respectively.

All the above dams are, or were, of the conventional earthwork with a watertight (clay) core, with the exception of the second Bilberry Dam which has an upstream clay outside skin [the first Bilberry Dam burst during the night of 4-5 February 1852 to cause, as also was the later failure of the Dale Dyke Dam *(vide supra)*, a major disaster resulting in considerable loss of life and property]. Masonry as a building medium was not to be introduced for the area's dams until the implementation of what was, without doubt, the most spectacular scheme involving the flooding of a Peak District valley, namely the upper Derwent Valley, resulting from work effected by the Derwent Valley Water Board (DVWB) (now part of Severn-Trent Water) between 1901 and 1916.

The DVWB – Its Incorporation and Terms of Reference

It was during the final decade of the nineteenth century that Derby, Leicester, Nottingham and Sheffield all separately began to consider the water resources of the upper Derwent Valley and the lower Ashop Valley, along with the annual rainfall of some fifty inches on the watersheds of the River Derwent and its tributary the River Ashop, as a heaven-sent provision. However, after allowing for the release of the compensation water [*i.e.* the water that the DVWB was - under Section 51 of the Derwent Valley Water Act of 1899 (*vide infra*) and in order to minimize, as much as possible, damage caused to owners of the lands and mills on the downstream stretches of the river – to have a statutory obligation to release into the River Derwent downstream of its dams at a uniform and continuous flow throughout the 24 hours of every day equivalent to $^{1}/_{365}$th part of one third of the total annual available rainfall for the drainage area above their reservoirs], the total available quantity of water was estimated to be only about thirty three million gallons per day (150 Ml/d).

Consequently, it was soon accepted that the several interested parties, which also came to include the counties of Derbyshire, Leicestershire and Nottinghamshire, could not have all the water they wished for, although, from the outset, it was recognized that Derbyshire merited special treatment since the source was almost wholly within that county and the River Derwent flowed for nearly its whole course through it. Conferences were therefore held to attempt to adjust the various claims accordingly but without success. As a result, separate Bills seeking parliamentary sanction for the sole control of the waters, with power to construct dams as necessary and to carry away the water from the reservoirs, were, in 1898 severally promoted by Derby, Leicester and Sheffield, with separate surveys being made and works being designed by their engineers, T. & C. Hawksley, Messrs Everard & Pick, and Edward M. Eaton, respectively.

Clearly, this situation provided a potentially fierce legislative battleground and contained all the materials for a protracted parliamentary fight. In the promotion of their separate Bills, the three corporations were acting not only independently but were in mutual opposition. Their individual endeavours were also opposed by Nottingham Corporation and the three county councils and also, extremely vigorously, by the owners of mills downstream of the proposed dams. The ultimate referral of all three Bills to the same parliamentary committee brought to a head the conflicting claims to rights in these waters. After a long battle at Westminster, the chairman of the parliamentary committee examining these claims, Sir John Brunner (then the MP for the Northwich Division of Cheshire), intimated that the interested parties should come to an understanding and that, if they could embody their claims in one Bill, suggested that its passage through the House of Commons would be smoothed by suspending Standing Orders so that the Bill might proceed within that session.

Thus it was that on 9 August 1899 the first Derwent Valley Water Act received the Royal Assent and by it the DVWB was incorporated, and various works were set out. Of the Board's total membership of thirteen, the representation amongst the four corporations was Derby (three), Leicester (four), Nottingham (two) and Sheffield (three) which was also in the same ratio as the water to be taken and the costs to be borne. Derbyshire had one member on the Board and from the supply could have a daily allocation of five million gallons (23 Ml/d). The County Council was not to contribute to the cost but local authorities in the County were to pay, in perpetuity, a sum equal to four percent on such proportion of the cost of the works as the water they took bore to the total amount of water supplied.

The plans as presented with the 1899 Act were rather a hotchpotch, selected from the three separate sets of plans that had been deposited previously with the original Bills. Not surprisingly, Edward Sandeman, upon his appointment as the DVWB's Engineer, found that the arrangements of these works, gathered as

The head offices of the DVWB that were constructed at Bamford during 1901 and 1902 and first occupied on 19 November 1902. A staff club was built on land at the rear and was opened by the then Chairman of the Board on the evening of Monday, 8 June 1903. With the DVWB's absorption into the Severn-Trent Water Authority on 1 April 1974, these currently extant buildings passed into the ownership of the latter organisation and, along with the adjoining land that had formerly accommodated the "Waterworks' Sidings" (vide infra), were sold into private ownership in 1987.

they had been from different sources, could be improved upon and, as a result of his advice, an amendment to the 1899 Act was sought, and effected by the Derwent Valley Water Act of 1901.

The new Act, whilst retaining the principle that the overall works should be undertaken in three instalments, modified their nature. Thus the originally proposed Derwent Dam was moved about ¼ mile higher up the Derwent Valley; its height was increased from 89 to 114 feet above river level, and its length by 30 feet, with its impounding capacity being increased accordingly. The result was that as much water would be impounded in the new Derwent Reservoir as would have been impounded in the combination of the Ronksley Reservoir (the reservoir at the highest altitude in the Derwent Valley under the terms of the 1899 Act) and the originally proposed Derwent Reservoir, thereby obviating the need for the former.

Thus the first instalment of the works was to involve the construction of the Howden and Derwent Dams in the Derwent Valley, together with an aqueduct which was to include seven miles of gravity cut-and-cover conduit of internal diameter 6 feet 3 inches, 3.7 miles of gravity tunnel lined with a ring of bricks with backing concrete, with a section practically the same as that of the cut-and-cover, and 17.4 miles of 45 inches diameter cast-iron or steel pressure pipes in inverted siphons and a filtration system at Bamford. This arrangement was to deliver the water by gravitation and via a covered service reservoir (of 28 million gallons capacity) at Ambergate, 28.1 miles away. Just beyond here – about two miles to the northwest of Heage – the aqueduct is divided into two branches on its journey southward. One of these, which includes a spur – about ¾ mile long and 28 inches in diameter – from near Coxbench to Little Eaton where it feeds into the Derby water grid, is laid for some 17¾ miles to the Derbyshire county border at Sawley, just to the south of Breaston from where, at Leicester's expense, it was linked into that city's water grid some 14 miles distant. The other branch main is laid for 7⅝ miles from Ambergate to the Derbyshire county border at Langley Mill from where it was continued, at Nottingham's expense, into that city's water grid. Final plans for the aqueduct were not sanctioned until the Derwent Valley Water Act of 1904. The supplies for various areas of Derbyshire are abstracted from the aqueduct where appropriate and the supply for Sheffield is abstracted upstream of the filtration plant – close to what is now the fishery office near the Ladybower Viaduct – from where it is conveyed by gravitation into Sheffield's reservoirs at Rivelin through a 4½ miles long tunnel that was constructed at that city's expense.

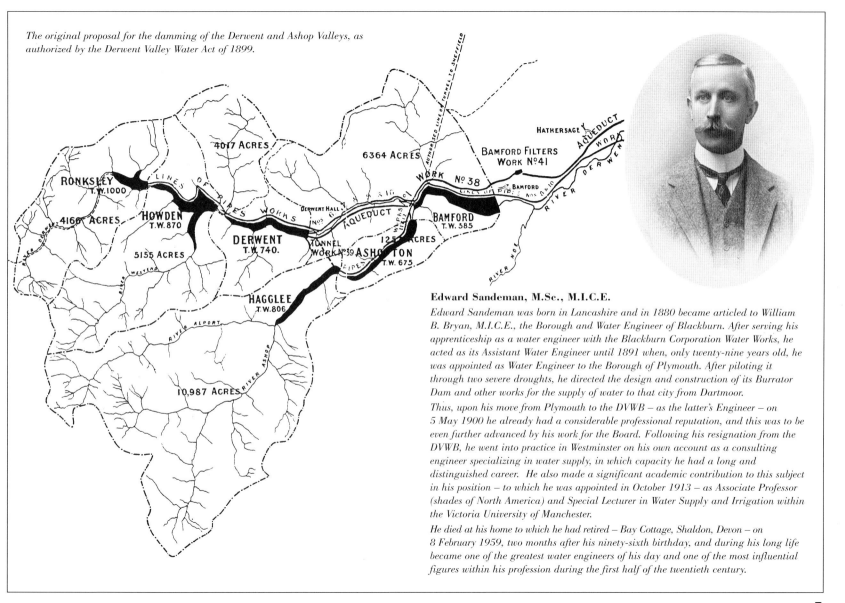

The original proposal for the damming of the Derwent and Ashop Valleys, as authorized by the Derwent Valley Water Act of 1899.

4017 ACRES

6364 ACRES

HATHERSAGE

AUTHORISED LINE OF TUNNEL TO SHEFFIELD

BAMFORD FILTERS WORK Nº41

WORK Nº 38

RONKSLEY T.W.1000

LINES OF PIPES

WORKS

Bamford Nºs 6 AND 10

RIVER DERWENT

WORK

4166 ACRES

HOWDEN T.W. 870

DERWENT HALL WORKS Nºs 6

LINES OF PIPES

LINES OF PIPES WORKS Nºs 9 AND 10

BAMFORD T.W. 585

RIVER DERWENT

AQUEDUCT

DERWENT T.W. 740.

5155 ACRES

TUNNEL WORK Nº39

125 ACRES

ASHOPTON T.W. 675.

RIVER NOE

RIVER WESTEND

RIVER DERWENT

PIPES

HAGGLEE T.W.806

RIVER ALPORT

10,987 ACRES

RIVER ASHOP

Edward Sandeman, M.Sc., M.I.C.E.

Edward Sandeman was born in Lancashire and in 1880 became articled to William B. Bryan, M.I.C.E., the Borough and Water Engineer of Blackburn. After serving his apprenticeship as a water engineer with the Blackburn Corporation Water Works, he acted as its Assistant Water Engineer until 1891 when, only twenty-nine years old, he was appointed as Water Engineer to the Borough of Plymouth. After piloting it through two severe droughts, he directed the design and construction of its Burrator Dam and other works for the supply of water to that city from Dartmoor.

Thus, upon his move from Plymouth to the DVWB – as the latter's Engineer – on 5 May 1900 he already had a considerable professional reputation, and this was to be even further advanced by his work for the Board. Following his resignation from the DVWB, he went into practice in Westminster on his own account as a consulting engineer specializing in water supply, in which capacity he had a long and distinguished career. He also made a significant academic contribution to this subject in his position – to which he was appointed in October 1913 – as Associate Professor (shades of North America) and Special Lecturer in Water Supply and Irrigation within the Victoria University of Manchester.

He died at his home to which he had retired – Bay Cottage, Shaldon, Devon – on 8 February 1959, two months after his ninety-sixth birthday, and during his long life became one of the greatest water engineers of his day and one of the most influential figures within his profession during the first half of the twentieth century.

A part of the cut-and-cover section of the aqueduct as it was being constructed on 20 October 1905 at Rowsley by Morrison and Mason Ltd., of Glasgow, working under contract for the DVWB.

8

Laying the last of the 45-inches diameter cast-iron pipes, on 7 October 1909, to complete the section of the aqueduct between the Derwent Dam and Grindleford.

Unlike the construction of the two dams and the Howden to Derwent aqueduct *(vide infra)* and the operation of the Bole Hill Quarry *(vide infra)*, which were all carried out by administration, that is by the DVWB's own employees, the construction of the main supply aqueduct together with the filtration system at Bamford and the service reservoir at Ambergate was effected under the operation of five separate contracts, but under the overall control of the DVWB.

The second instalment of the works was to involve the construction of the Hagglee Dam in the Ashop Valley. The project was to be completed by the construction of the Ashopton and Bamford dams, the water from which, being too low for gravitational flow down the aqueduct, was to be used primarily for compensation purposes, thereby releasing the greater proportion of the water in the higher reservoirs for town supply by gravitation, although water in the two lowest reservoirs could be pumped into the aqueduct if required.

In the event, the three dams proposed for the second and third instalments were never built. A detailed geological examination of the Ashop Valley (including the sinking of trial pits) made during the 1920s was to show that it was unsuitable for the impounding of the proposed reservoirs and therefore, as the second instalment of its works, the DVWB adopted the proposal that had been unique to Sheffield Corporation's original parliamentary submission, namely that the upper waters of the River Ashop should be made available for town supply by gravitation, by diverting them into the Derwent Reservoir. This was to be achieved by means of a weir built across the River Ashop just above its confluence with the River Alport (SK141893) [the waters of which were also to be diverted into the pool of the Ashop weir via a smaller weir (SK141897) built across it just above the confluence] and a watercourse, including a tunnel under the ridge between the Ashop and the Derwent Valleys.

A similar approach was to be taken much later when the catchment area of the Ladybower Reservoir *(vide infra)* was increased by diverting into it the waters from the River Noe, near to Nether Booth Farm in the Edale Valley, and from

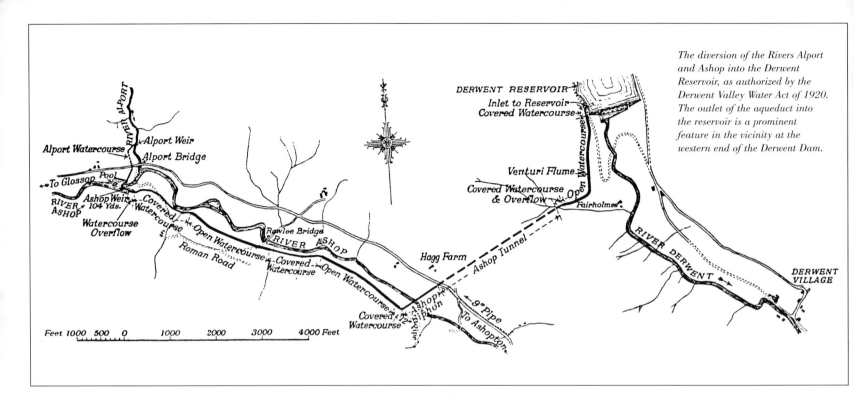

Peakshole Water, ½ mile east of Castleton, and Bradwell Brook, ½ mile northeast of the centre of Bradwell. These two schemes – which were formally inaugurated on 18 April 1951 and 7 July 1960, respectively – differ essentially in that whereas the former functions by gravitation the latter required an electrically-operated pumping facility. However, the final sections of the aqueduct in both consists of a concrete-lined tunnel which passes through the ridge that divides the Edale and Ashop Valleys and beneath Win Hill, respectively, and which discharge into the Ashop branch of the reservoir at SK 166873 and SK 182861, respectively.

Perhaps surprisingly, Ronksley Reservoir, abandoned in favour of an enlarged Derwent Reservoir under the terms of the Act of 1901, never re-emerged as a serious proposal. However, it may have evoked such hostility that it probably would have foundered.

Their ultimate purchase of Derwent Hall was to permit the DVWB to flood the Derwent Valley, including the hall and most of the village of Derwent, and the Ashop Valley for some 2 miles beyond Ashopton – and including this village. This was to result from the implementation of the third instalment of the DVWB's modified works, namely the construction, between 1935 and 1946, of the Ladybower Dam about a mile upstream from the proposed Bamford Dam. This possible replacement scenario had originally been suggested by Edward Sandeman in his report to the DVWB on 21 August 1900, when he recognized it, however, as being dependent upon the acquisition of Derwent Hall. Ladybower Dam now reverted to being an earth embankment with a clay core and impounded a reservoir of 6,300 million gallons capacity, slightly greater than the combined total that would have been impounded by the originally proposed Hagglee, Ashopton and Bamford Dams. Like the reservoirs that would have been impounded by the latter two proposed dams, the primary purpose of that at Ladybower is to provide compensation water in order to permit more of the water in the Howden and Derwent Reservoirs to be made available for supply by gravitation although, if required, water in the Ladybower Reservoir can be pumped into the aqueduct for town supply.

The Masonry – Source and Transport

Unlike the second and third instalments of its proposed works, the first instalment of the DVWB's undertaking in the upper reaches of the Derwent Valley closely adhered to the proposals presented in the Acts of 1901 and 1904. In addition, and mindful of the failures of the Bilberry and Dale Dyke Dams in the vicinity some few years earlier *(vide supra)*, and that the security of the structures was of prime importance – with the cost of the works assuming a secondary position – the DVWB accepted Sandeman's suggestion that the Howden and Derwent Dams should be constructed of masonry.

Consequently, in order to obtain the necessary building stone, millstone grit, the DVWB, after several possible sites had been turned down for environmental reasons, opened up a quarry on a fifty-two acre site that it purchased – from a Mr. Shuttleworth from Hathersage - at Bole Hill on the hillside above Grindleford Station on the Midland Railway which had between Dore and Chinley been opened on 1 June 1894. In order that the stone could be transported without

transshipment from the quarry to the dam construction sites, the former was serviced by a standard gauge railway system on which the stone was carried via an incline – the first wagon loaded with stone destined for the Derwent Valley being sent down the incline on 23 May 1903 - into a siding at Grindleford from where it was transported on the Midland Railway, using the Midland's own engines, for some five miles to Thornhill, just beyond Bamford Station.

The winding drum at the top of the incline which drops away to the photographer's left. The cutting – seen half left – carries the standard gauge railway out of Bole Hill Quarry to the incline. The drum's stone supporting structure can still be located at the site and a walk around the quarry site (SK 248794), now owned by the National Trust, is of interest and well worthwhile, with many large stones that were quarried but not ultimately used being readily identified by the indentations that had been used in their gripping by the "stone dogs" (callipers pulled tight by a load on a chain during lifting).

Looking up the railway incline toward Bole Hill Quarry from near to the siding to the immediate west of Grindleford Station. A wagon load of large stones is descending and is at the same time hauling the distant empty wagon up the hill, via the cable passing over the winding drum. The speed of the connected wagons was controlled by Tom Green who operated the brake on the drum. At the upper right can be seen parts of some of the bungalows that were erected for those workmen at the site who required housing. The course of the incline, the lower end of which now passes beneath the lane at Upper Padley (SK 246790), can still be readily located, as can the remains of the foundations of the bungalows.

Here there was constructed another siding – the "Waterworks' Sidings" – from which, when working under contract for the DVWB, Walter Scott and Co. and later their successor, Messrs Walter Scott and Middleton Ltd., laid some seven miles of standard gauge single track with passing loops – the Bamford & Howden Railway - along the western bank of the River Derwent, and northwest to the Howden construction site, with a spur off to the Derwent construction site.

The DVWB's locomotive "Togo" hauling a train of flat wagons carrying large stones from Bole Hill Quarry, on the Bamford & Howden Railway and about half-a-mile north of "Waterworks' Sidings". The lane shown to the right is Carr Lane, that runs from Yorkshire Bridge to Thornhill. Although the bridge carrying the railway and that over the railway in the background have both now been demolished, this stretch of the railway's embankment is still readily recognizable and, in common with many other of the Peak District's disused railways, the bed of the track on either side of the lane has been converted into public footpaths.

The most southerly of the three viaducts on the Bamford & Howden Railway was at Ashopton and is seen here in July 1904 as it carried the line over the River Ashop at its confluence with the River Derwent, seen flowing down from the lower right. The junction of the lane with the main Sheffield to Manchester road can be seen about one third the way up the far right side. This area now lies deep beneath the Ladybower Reservoir and some 200 yards south of the western end of the present Ashopton Viaduct that carries the present A57 main road. The DVWB's locomotive – either "King" or "Queen" – is hauling a train of loaded wagons, of the type especially designed for carrying small stones, northward up the Derwent Valley. The other two viaducts were of a similar design – namely a superstructure of pitch-pine trestles supported on masonry foundations, with that at Ashopton also being, of necessity, of steel spans over the River Ashop and the main road from Sheffield to Manchester – and carried the line over the tributary valley of the Locker Brook at Fairholmes (where its foundations can be located on the opposite side of the road from the exit from the public car park) and the Ouzelden Clough (where the residual end timbers can still be seen and where the stone foundations become a prominent feature in the landscape when the level of the Derwent Reservoir falls accordingly). Other features of the railway are still apparent in that its course can be located in many places on the lower side of the present road up the valley and, beyond the Derwent Dam, the straight stretch of the road is laid on its track bed, as also is the road between the northern end of the site of Birchinlee village and the western tower of the Howden Dam.

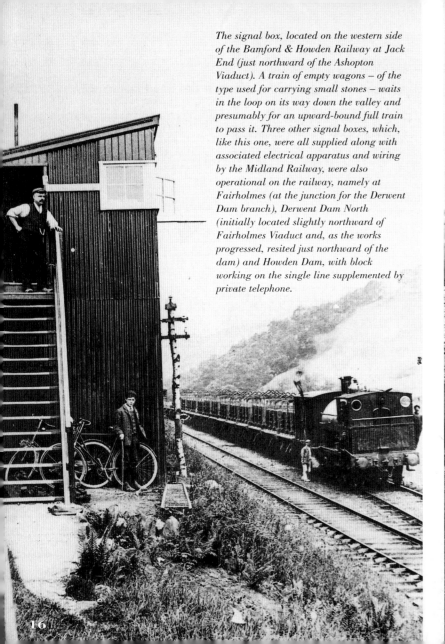

The signal box, located on the western side of the Bamford & Howden Railway at Jack End (just northward of the Ashopton Viaduct). A train of empty wagons – of the type used for carrying small stones – waits in the loop on its way down the valley and presumably for an upward-bound full train to pass it. Three other signal boxes, which, like this one, were all supplied along with associated electrical apparatus and wiring by the Midland Railway, were also operational on the railway, namely at Fairholmes (at the junction for the Derwent Dam branch), Derwent Dam North (initially located slightly northward of Fairholmes Viaduct and, as the works progressed, resited just northward of the dam) and Howden Dam, with block working on the single line supplemented by private telephone.

Looking northeastward down the spur from the main line of the Bamford & Howden Railway toward the Derwent Dam construction site on 26 June 1905. The stone pillars that supported the superstructure of the bridge over the river can still be seen – down to the right of the footpath immediately upon leaving the public car park at Fairholmes en-route to the downstream face of the Derwent Dam.

"Long" George Green, the author's late maternal grandfather, is seen here operating a crane that is unloading the 3-ton capacity containers that have carried small stones from Bole Hill Quarry (vide supra) on their especially designed wagons to their destination in the Derwent Valley. Whilst a container was held in the air by a crane over the dump heap, a catch was loosened on it, causing it to turn over by reason of its own weight and empty its contents, a strong spiral spring then causing it to revolve automatically back into its normal level position.

DERWENT VALLEY
WATER BOARD
220

The completion of the railway – which as well as building stone also carried coal, bags of cement and other essential supplies to the building sites – to the Howden terminal siding, with spurs down to and through the dam, was effected by 23 January 1903 and in the following April, the DVWB extended this northern head of the line by 330 yards to the proposed site of the Howden stone yard. At Howden, an engine shed, with an inspection well for locomotives, was installed by 21 February 1903 and, by early 1903, workshops for engineer fitters, blacksmiths and carpenters had also been erected nearby and close to Marebottom farmhouse.

The 50h.p. compound engine, manufactured by Rushton, Proctor and Company, that was installed at Howden in January 1904.

The western side of the Howden construction site in November 1904. The building in the foreground housed the 50h.p. compound engine that supplied power to the stone crushers (immediately to the left), the machinery in the engineering and fitting workshop (the building at the photograph's far left) and for driving the air compressor (which supplied power for the drills and some of the water pumps).

Feeding the stone crushers at the Howden site. The concrete foundations of this machinery are close to the northwestern side of the Howden Dam and become visible as the reservoir's level falls accordingly, whereas the corresponding foundations at Derwent are somewhat further away from the dam – being about 25 yards on the far side of the outlet of the aqueduct from the diversion of the Rivers Alport and Ashop – but are permanently visible as three concrete pillars that protrude above the reservoir's top water level.

Inside the engineering and fitting workshop at Howden.
The installed machinery included a hammer, a lathe and
a drill, all of which were steam-powered.

Howden Fitter

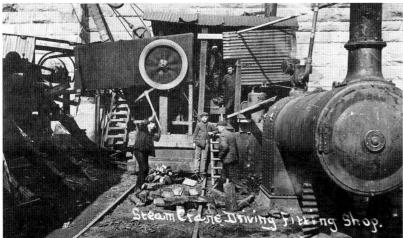

Steam Crane Driving Fitting Shop.

Above: Blacksmiths at work in the engineering and fitting workshop at Howden.

Left: The steam-crane, as it was adapted for driving the machinery in the nearby engineering and fitting workshop at Howden circa 1910, by which time the workshop had been isolated from its former source of power – the 50h.p. compound engine – by the then intervening western side of the dam, the downstream face of which can be seen in the background.

Over its productive life of about 7$\frac{1}{2}$ years, a total of just over 1.2 million tons of stone was sent to the two dam construction sites from the Bole Hill Quarry. A plan of the quarry site, with particular emphasis upon the layout of its component railway, is presented by Bowtell on page 82 of his excellent book.

The Manual Labour Force and its Accommodation

Between April 1902 and November 1903, the Board's total workforce, which included men employed in the Bole Hill Quarry, on the construction of the various sections of the aqueduct and on other works distant from the actual construction sites of the two dams, remained between 600 to 700 although its numbers then increased on a fairly regular basis, exceeding 1,000 for the first time during October 1904, 1500 during April 1906, 2000 during December 1907 and 2500 during May 1908, with the maximum number of 2,753 workers being reached during June 1908. From then on the numbers gradually declined, dropping below 1,000 for the first time during October 1910 and below 500 during November 1913. Although some of the Board's manual labour force were local men, the majority of it was, in common with other groups employed upon the construction of public works around the turn of the nineteenth century, drawn from the group of men known as navvies, a name that evolved from the navigators, the workmen who had been responsible for the digging and construction of the navigations (canals) in earlier times. These men, from whose work the engineers took the glory and the entrepreneurs took the profit, were a nomadic group (the majority of those employed by the DVWB had been previously employed on the construction of dams – by Birmingham Corporation – in the Elan Valley, near Rhayader in mid-Wales) who, along with their families, were estimated in 1908 to number 100,000 persons. The abuse of this itinerant labour force by employers was widespread – as manifest, for example, during the early days of railway construction in this country when the accommodation available to the large numbers of immigrant workers and their wives and children was either disgraceful or non-existent, other conditions of their employment were often shameful, and little, if any, attention was paid to their physical, educational, moral or spiritual requirements. The problem arose not only because of the employers' indifference but also because public building works usually necessitated immigration into the area of a body of men, some with wives and children. Indeed, dam construction sites were situated in remote and mountainous localities, far from towns and villages where accommodation might be available or where new housing might be built by the contractors for lease to their employees. This was the situation facing the DVWB with regard to the housing of the navvies who were to be employed in the construction of the Howden and Derwent Dams and, in fact, under Section 64 of the Derwent Valley Water Act of 1899 the Board had a statutory obligation to provide a satisfactory environment for the care and accommodation of its employees. In conformity with this, it constructed a temporary village between the two construction sites, situated about $^1/_2$ mile to the south of the Howden site, and named Birchinlee, since it was built on land forming part of a farm by that name. However, it acquired the widely-used nickname of "Tin Town" or "Tin City" because its buildings, both domestic and public, had corrugated iron outside walls, although they were lined with wood and fitted with coal-burning fires, essential comforts during the rigours of a Peak District winter at an altitude of some 800 feet. This village was well-provided with shops and public services, including a railway station and freely-available passenger train service on the railway that ran from "Waterworks' Sidings" to the Howden construction site, at the height of activity on the project – between mid 1908 and mid 1912 – it had a maximum population of around just over 900, and in providing it the DVWB thoroughly met its obligations imposed under Section 64 of the 1899 Act. However, typical of its thriftiness, it made an overall profit from this village enterprise.

Looking northward up the upper Derwent Valley in early 1912 from the southeastern slopes of the Ouzelden Clough. To the left is the village of Birchinlee, in the background stands the almost complete Howden Dam, south of which flows the River Derwent. To the immediate right of the river is part of the road that originally ran all the way up the valley and in the right foreground can be seen the northern part of the viaduct which crossed over the Ouzelden Clough and carried the Bamford & Howden Railway (vide supra), the course of which can be readily discerned along the eastern extremity of the village. Within a few years, the river, road and viaduct's foundations, but not the site of the village, would be submerged beneath the Derwent Reservoir. In the left foreground is the treatment plant for the sewage effluent from the village, the accommodation in which was serviced by water toilets, still an unusual domestic feature in the early twentieth century.

23

The Construction of the Dams

Excavations for the foundations of the Howden Dam began on 16 July 1901 and for the Derwent Dam on 18 July 1902. Prior to this, cableways – each with a carrying capacity of 6 tons, with spans of 1,385 feet and 1,525 feet, respectively, and in each case a sag of about 80 feet and a height above the river of some 150 feet - had been erected (by Messrs J. M. Henderson and Co., of Aberdeen, working under contract from the DVWB's blueprints) to span and service both sites.

Looking eastward on 21 April 1904 along the cableways that spanned the Derwent site. In the left and right foregrounds are the static and mobile support towers of the north and south cableways, respectively, which are linked to their corresponding mobile and static support towers on the opposite side of the valley. At the far left can be seen the doss-house and the single-story building toward the mid-right is the DVWB's on-site office.

The northern cableway's static support tower – that, like all such towers, was fixed and anchored to a concrete block in the ground – and the associated engine house at the western side of the Derwent site.

The mobile support tower at the eastern end of the northern cableway that spanned the Derwent site. The associated lifting gear can be seen suspended from the cables, and the tower's balance box, that would have been filled with large stones, is discernable at its bottom right, namely at the rear of the structure. The roof of the doss-house is also clearly visible. A cableway unit system covered a triangular area of ground but, by placing the mobile ends of the two systems on opposite sides of the valley, the total area of ground covered by the pair became rectangular. The former sites of the cableways' support towers can still be located on the banks at the eastern and western ends of the two dams.

Work on the excavations progressed well despite the ingress of considerable amounts of water which was removed, sometimes at a rate approaching a million gallons per day, by the continual operation of several pumps, although sometimes the rate of percolation exceeded that of pumping and brought the digging to a temporary halt. Another setback during the excavations occurred when an unexpected geological feature was uncovered at both sites. These large"wrinkles", thought to be the result of land movement caused by the weight of the surrounding hills compressing the Yoredale shales in the valley bottom and forcing them to crumple, were neither watertight nor strong enough to found the dams on, and had therefore to be excavated to reach solid rock suitable for the foundations. Not only did this additional work delay the project's completion by several months, but it also increased its cost. On account of the additional excavation further building material was required and as a result the amount of stone taken from Bole Hill Quarry was 50% more than originally had been estimated. Nevertheless, even when sufficiently solid rock was reached, it was still not watertight. However, rather than extend the full width of the dams' foundations, which would have entailed the provision of even more building materials, it was decided to adopt the more economical expedient and in each case excavate a "heel trench" some six feet wide extending below the foundation level down to watertight strata. This "trench" was then filled with concrete, to act as a cut-off to prevent water from flowing underneath the dam.

The "wrinkle" as excavated at the upstream face of the trench at the Derwent site by 11 September 1904. Cross sections were measured at intervals of 25 feet across both dams, beginning from their western ends. For example, on the Derwent Dam – being 1,000 feet long – forty such sections were recorded. Thus, C.S.14, C.S.15 and C.S.16 on the boards illustrated indicate that, at Derwent, the "wrinkle" was positioned between cross sections 14 and 16, namely from 350 to 400 feet from the dam's western end. The numbers on the right of the boards (620, 640, 660) indicate their elevation, in feet, above ordnance datum. Subsequent introduction of high pressure cement grouting to effect their stabilization – after they had been detected via boreholes – obviated the necessity to excavate – and thereby expose – these geological features and therefore this illustration is of a particular significance and interest.

Above: Excavation work at the Howden site was halted altogether when, as a result of a rainfall of 2 inches on 17 October 1907, the River Derwent broke its banks and flooded the whole of the trench on the eastern side. It took four days to pump out the main foundations.

Left: A Tangyes water pump in use in the excavations for the Howden Dam during 1903.

Looking eastward across the Derwent site as excavated by September 1904. Clearly discernable are the top of the "heel trench", the former bed of the River Derwent (now diverted around the far eastern side of the site), the doss-house (upper left) and the DVWB's on-site office (upper right).

Above: Samuel George Hallett, the site foreman (right), with two members of his workforce in the "heel trench" at Howden inspecting the progress of the concrete infilling on 1 July 1904.

Right: Part of the "heel trench" that lay exposed at the Howden site on 19 September 1906, by which time other sections of the "trench" in the more central positions had, in fact, already been excavated, filled with concrete and built over.

Once the difficulties with the foundations had been overcome, work continued as expected for several years. The heart of both dams consists of large displacers, or "plums" as they were called, comprising undressed stones varying in weight from one to six tons, which were embedded in concrete, with the stone forming about 44% of the whole mass. No two "plums" when set in this manner touched each other and all were carefully washed before being put into place to ensure perfect adhesion between stone and concrete. The outside surfaces of both the upstream and downstream faces of both dams that are below ground

Washing "plums" at the Howden site. A major difference between the two dams is that whereas most of the "dog holes" on the exposed surfaces of the masonry in the Derwent Dam have been dressed out, those in the Howden Dam either remain untouched or have only been crudely removed, a feature readily apparent around the doorway at the base of the eastern tower of the dam.

The construction at the Howden site by 26 June 1905. The "plums" set in the concrete and the lower and the beginnings of the upper facing stones in this section of the base of the dam's downstream face are of particular interest in this photograph. Note also the angle gauge in the foreground.

level are of roughly squared undressed stones whereas dressed stone, rectangular or squared and averaging three feet in thickness was used for faces that are above ground level. The joints between these facing stones are ³/₄ inch wide and, on the upstream side, they were caulked with neat cement slightly damped with water, the caulking being kept back a little from the pitch-line to prevent damage by frost. Beginning with those almost mid-way across the valley, as each section of the excavations met, upon inspection by either Sandeman or an appropriate member of his staff, the requisite criteria, building upon them commenced. Thus the masonry structure of both dams rose from the middle of the valley and grew upward and outward toward the valley sides.

Stone masons at work at the Howden site. The man with the hammer in the foreground was one of the skilled tradesmen who had followed Edward Sandeman from the completed Burrator Dam construction project in Devon. He was John Creber, a granite mason, who was originally from Walkhampton, Devon.

The Howden Dam as constructed by: 11 May 1906. Looking eastward.

Above: 25 April 1907. Looking northward. The larger of the buildings at the upper left is the aerating shed in which cement could be spread out in thin layers and turned in order to improve its working properties.

Above, right: 23 July 1908. Looking westward. Some half-way down and fairly central in the structure can be seen the entrance to the passage, an inspection tunnel with a cross section of 3 feet by 7 feet 6 inches that connects the two towers from their lower areas. As expected, a similar tunnel runs through the Derwent Dam.

Right: 2 September 1909. Looking westward. In the upstream face of the nearest partially built tower can be seen the five pairs of openings that are so placed to permit water to be taken for supply at any level or from any depth beneath the surface of the reservoir, and the three lower apertures through which, along with three similar openings in the base of the other tower, the reservoir can be emptied into the immediately downstream Derwent Reservoir.

Left: The Derwent Dam as constructed by:
Top left: 24 April 1907. Looking westward. On the west bank and directly behind the construction can be seen the cement aerating shed similar to that at the Howden site. The concrete pillars, in this instance supporting a supply line into the site from the right, were a feature at both construction sites, where they were ultimately built into the dams' internal structures.
Top right: 12 November 1908. The outlet pipework for future supply purposes, as then constructed in the base of what was to be the eastern tower.
Below left: 7 May 1909. Looking eastward. Upstream of the site on the lower (original) road passing up the valley, the first group of buildings reached are those of Hollinclough Farm and the second are those of Hancock Farm. The ruins, as piles of stones, of both those farms become visible when the level of the Derwent Reservoir falls accordingly.
Below right; 19 June 1912. Looking westward. The downstream exits from the railway tunnel and the River Derwent's culvert that then passed through the dam are clearly visible.

In order to permit the excavation to proceed across the bed of the River Derwent at both sites, the river was initially diverted around their eastern extremities, and ultimately directed through a culvert that was built into each of the dams. Another temporary passage built into each of the dams was a tunnel at ground level, large enough to allow the passage of a locomotive and thereby to permit communication between the upstream and downstream sides of the dam which would have been difficult after the masonry rose above ground level. Both the culverts and tunnels were ultimately filled in and sealed.

Looking westward across the Howden site in October 1902, a view that gives some idea of the scale of the excavations in which a small army of workmen are involved. The diverted River Derwent flows from right to left in the foreground and the two cableways are also clearly visible - with that to the south lifting material from the excavations - and their individual engine houses can be seen at the photograph's extreme left and right sides. Each of the four cableways that covered both sites was driven, via its western support tower, by an individual steam engine.

The winding drum inside one of the cableway engine houses at Howden.

Left: The Howden Dam as constructed by 11 May 1906, showing the entrance to the temporary culvert for the diverted River Derwent and the upstream exit from the temporary railway tunnel that then passed through the dam from its downstream face.

Below left: Sealing the upstream face, circa September 1914, of the River Derwent's former culvert that passed through the Derwent Dam.

On 21 June 1907, record stones were laid above the doorways at the base of the then partially built western towers of the Howden and Derwent Dams.

Below: The laying of the record stone on the partially construced Derwent Dam on 21 June 1907. The stone can be located above the doorway at the foot of the dam's western tower.

Right: Thomas Gainsford, the then Chairman of the DVWB, laying the record stone on the partially constructed Howden Dam on 21 June 1907. The stone, albeit now somewhat corroded by water seepage through the dam, can be located above the doorway at the foot of the dam's western tower. Standing immediately to Gainsford's right is Samuel George Hallett, the foreman at the Howden site, to the immediate right of the stone is Edward Sandeman, the DVWB's Engineer, to the left of the photograph can be seen a group of children from Birchinlee school in their Sunday best and standing immediately on their left, the man in the suit and with the short beard is George Eustace Sutton, the navvy missioner at the village.

THE HOWDEN RESERVOIR
This Howden Reservoir
was built by the
Derby · Leicester · Nottingham · Sheffield
for the use of the people of
and Derbyshire.

37

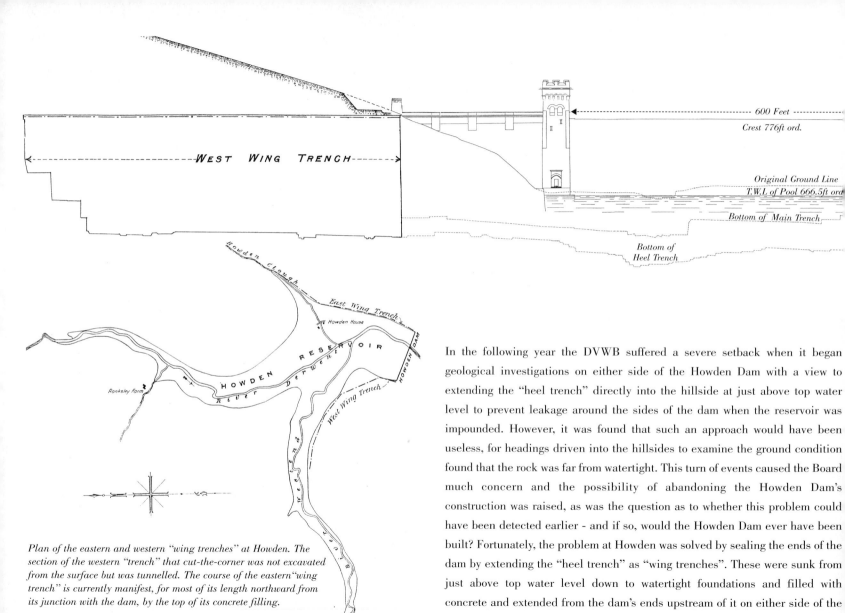

WEST WING TRENCH

600 Feet

Crest 776ft ord.

Original Ground Line
T.W.L of Pool 666.5ft ord

Bottom of Main Trench

Bottom of Heel Trench

Howden Clough

East Wing Trench

Howden House

HOWDEN RESERVOIR

River Derwent

HOWDEN DAM

Ronksley Farm

West Wing Trench

River Derwent

Plan of the eastern and western "wing trenches" at Howden. The section of the western "trench" that cut-the-corner was not excavated from the surface but was tunnelled. The course of the eastern "wing trench" is currently manifest, for most of its length northward from its junction with the dam, by the top of its concrete filling.

In the following year the DVWB suffered a severe setback when it began geological investigations on either side of the Howden Dam with a view to extending the "heel trench" directly into the hillside at just above top water level to prevent leakage around the sides of the dam when the reservoir was impounded. However, it was found that such an approach would have been useless, for headings driven into the hillsides to examine the ground condition found that the rock was far from watertight. This turn of events caused the Board much concern and the possibility of abandoning the Howden Dam's construction was raised, as was the question as to whether this problem could have been detected earlier - and if so, would the Howden Dam ever have been built? Fortunately, the problem at Howden was solved by sealing the ends of the dam by extending the "heel trench" as "wing trenches". These were sunk from just above top water level down to watertight foundations and filled with concrete and extended from the dam's ends upstream of it on either side of the

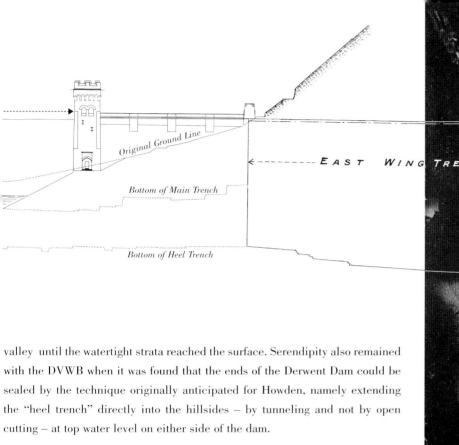

EAST WING TRENCH

Original Ground Line

Bottom of Main Trench

Bottom of Heel Trench

valley until the watertight strata reached the surface. Serendipity also remained with the DVWB when it was found that the ends of the Derwent Dam could be sealed by the technique originally anticipated for Howden, namely extending the "heel trench" directly into the hillsides – by tunneling and not by open cutting – at top water level on either side of the dam.

Above: Longitudinal section of the Derwent Dam, showing the depths of the excavations (main trench and "heel trench"), the heights of the masonry, and the "wing trenches". Although the visible section of the dam is, without doubt, an imposing castellated structure, the majority of it – in its "heel trench" and two "wing trenches" – is forever hidden from view.

Right: Miners at work inside the tunnelled section of the western "wing trench" at Howden. The absence of any protective head gear is particularly noticeable. The building of the Howden and Derwent Dams claimed a high cost in men either killed (eighteen) or seriously injured and mutilated in accidents, a price that could have been much higher than actually transpired in view of the hazardous nature of much of the work and the complete absence of any semblance of what are now regarded as essential practices governing safety at work.

The valves in the eastern tower of the Howden Dam were first closed and the reservoir began to fill on 1 January 1912. The reservoir's water first overflowed the dam's crest on 22 July 1912. The dam was formally opened, amid much pomp and ceremony, on 5 September 1912, with the reservoir's water being made available for supply via the Howden to Derwent aqueduct, an enclosed water course that runs from the base of the eastern tower of the Howden Dam and down and just beyond the eastern side of the Derwent Reservoir to join the main supply aqueduct just downstream of the Derwent Dam's eastern tower.

On 30 September 1912, Edward Sandeman resigned as Engineer to the DVWB, although his services were retained in a consultative capacity. The demolition of Birchinlee village began in December 1912 (the final residents, who were the missioner and his family, left in early 1915), on 13 September 1914 the Bole Hill Quarry was closed, by the end of 1914 the demolition of the Bamford & Howden Railway, southward from its northern terminal at Howden had begun, and the filling of the Derwent Reservoir began on 19 November 1915. The water first overflowed the dam's crest on 8 January 1916 and the dam was opened, without any ceremony whatsoever, sometime during 1916, the exact date being unknown. Perhaps this was a reflection of either Britain's involvement at that time in the carnage of what was "the war to end all wars" or, after all the problems and setbacks it had encountered, the DVWB was only too pleased to accept the consummation of the first instalment of its works, the most ambitious combined water supply project of its time. Whatever may have been the reason(s) for it, this complete lack of ceremonial is compounded by the fact that the bringing into operation of the Derwent Reservoir is not referred to in the minutes of any of the meetings of the DVWB. Significant, also, in this respect, are the record stones that were laid at the partially constructed dams on the 21 June 1907, for whereas that at Howden subsequently had 1912, the year of its inauguration, added in the appropriate place, the corresponding area on the stone in the Derwent Dam remains blank – perhaps it should now be completed!

Samuel George Hallett, the foreman at Howden, had left the Board's service by the time the building of the Derwent Dam was completed. At this juncture, Charles Pickett, who had been foreman at the Derwent site since 1903, became Chief Foreman, in the Engineer's Department, of the Board's works in totality and was subsequently appointed as the foreman in charge of the construction of the Ashop Diversion, that was to comprise their second instalment. However, in March 1927, just a short time before its completion, he was forced to retire through illness. There is no doubt that Pickett made a major input into the first quarter century's works of the DVWB, a contribution that is recognized and commemorated by a stone, set into the wall to the left of the door when entering the upper section of the western tower of the Derwent Dam, on which is inscribed:

CHARLES PICKETT
FOREMAN OF WORKS
1903 TO 1926

It is unfortunate that Hallett's contribution is not likewise acknowledged at Howden, or anywhere else.

With the bringing into use of the Derwent Dam, and the fashioning and tidying of its immediate downstream area, the first instalment of the DVWB's works was completed and a total of 13·434 million gallons of water per 24 hours became available for supply. However, the total cost of this first phase of the works amounted to £3,560,350, far in excess of the figure that had been included in the original estimate of £5,500,000 for the completion of *all* the works authorized under the Act of 1901. Obviously, the unexpected setbacks had had a marked financial impact.

Right: Sir Edward H. Fraser, the then Chairman of the DVWB, in the act of officially opening the Howden Dam. The cleric standing to his immediate right rear is Dr. Edwin Hoskyns, the Bishop of Southwell, who led a short religious service on this occasion and during which he gave thanks for the successful completion of this instalment of the scheme and then offered prayers of dedication.

The Howden Dam on its opening day, 5 September 1912. On the left are the marquees in which the DVWB's officials and guests, and later their manual work force with their wives, were entertained to lunch and tea, respectively, after the opening ceremony, the site of which can be seen on the far right.

The officials and guests of the DVWB gathered for the opening of the Howden Dam.

Resident Engineers and Engineering Assistants and some other of the DVWB's staff gathered in the reception area during the opening of the Howden Dam. From left to right are William Francis Henry Creber, ?, Douglas Leslie Serpell, Charles Pickett (Derwent site foreman), Oswald Brierly Steward (Clerk and Solicitor to the Board), Samuel George Hallett (Howden site foreman), ?, A. H. Jameson, J. W. Wilkinson, ?, A. W. Robinson, Edward Sandeman (Engineer to the DVWB), W. H. M. Jameson, ?, Sidney Beaufoy Winser (Assistant Engineer to the DVWB), ?, Samuel Seager (Accountant to the Board), M. M. McCallum, Eric Hamilton Whiteford, ? and E. C. Winter. Behind them can be seen part of the Howden Dam and in particular its eastern tower.

The DVWB's workmen, their wives and the shopkeepers from Birchinlee at their celebration tea during the afternoon following the opening of the Howden Dam and after the Board's officials and guests had been entertained to lunch.

The children of Birchinlee at their celebration tea in the village's recreation hall on 5 September 1912. Each child in the village under the age of fourteen years was presented with a framed souvenir multiple photograph showing the village and the Howden works.

Specifications relating to the Howden and Derwent Dams and their impounded reservoirs

Consideration	Howden	Derwent
Length of the dam at top water level (in feet)	1,080	1,110
Thickness at the base of the dam (in feet)	176 [1]	171
Thickness at the crest of the overflow weir (in feet)	10	10
Height of the towers above the top water level (in feet)	50	50
Distance between the towers, *i.e.* the length of the overflow weir (in feet)	500	600
Height of the crest of the overflow weir from the former river level (in feet)	117	114
Height of the dam from the deepest part of the main trench to the overflow level (in feet)	187	174
Height of the dam from the deepest part of the heel trench to the overflow level (in feet)	242	212
Maximum depth of the reservoir (in feet)	116	106
Net storage capacity of the reservoir when first filled (in million gallons)	2,050 [2]	2,155
Top water level of the reservoir above ordnance-datum (in feet)	870	776
Area of the reservoir when full (in acres)	157	183
Length of the reservoir when full (in miles)	1¼	1¾
Area of the watershed (in acres)	9,321	3,899